Hans-Günter Heumann

Piano Junior

A Creative and Interactive
Piano Course for Children

Duet Book 2

ED 13822

Illustrations by Leopé

SCHOTT

Mainz · London · Berlin · Madrid · New York · Paris · Prague · Tokyo · Toronto
© 2016 SCHOTT MUSIC Ltd. London. Printed in Germany

ED 13822
British Library Cataloguing-in-Publication-Data.
A catalogue record for this book is available from the British Library.
ISMN 979-0-2201-3648-1
ISBN 978-1-84761-432-2

Cover illustration by Leopé (www.leope.com)
Cover design: www.adamhaystudio.com
Audio tracks recorded, mixed and mastered by Clements Pianos
Audio tracks performed by Samantha Ward and Maciej Raginia
Printed in Germany S&Co.9213

Contents

Please visit **www.piano-junior.com** to stream or download demo and play-along recordings for all the tunes in the book.

Secondo

1. The Organ Grinder

▶ Audio Track **1/2**

4

Primo

1. The Organ Grinder

HGH

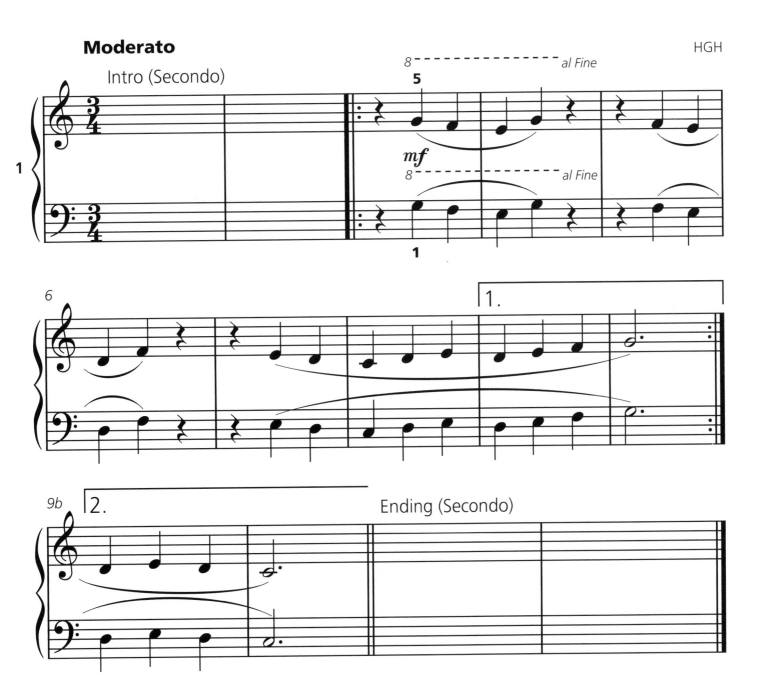

2. Carnival

Allegro ♩ = 200

f legato

Fine

mf

D. C. al Fine

▶ Audio Track **3/4**

2. Carnival

Allegro

Fine

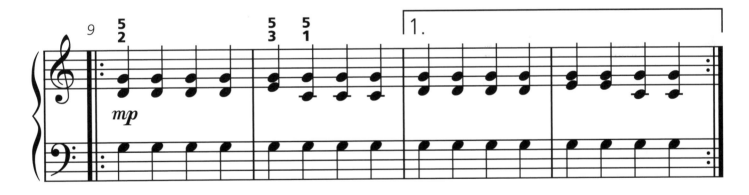

D. C. al Fine

3. Yankee Doodle

American Folk Song
Arr.: HGH

Allegro ♩ = 152

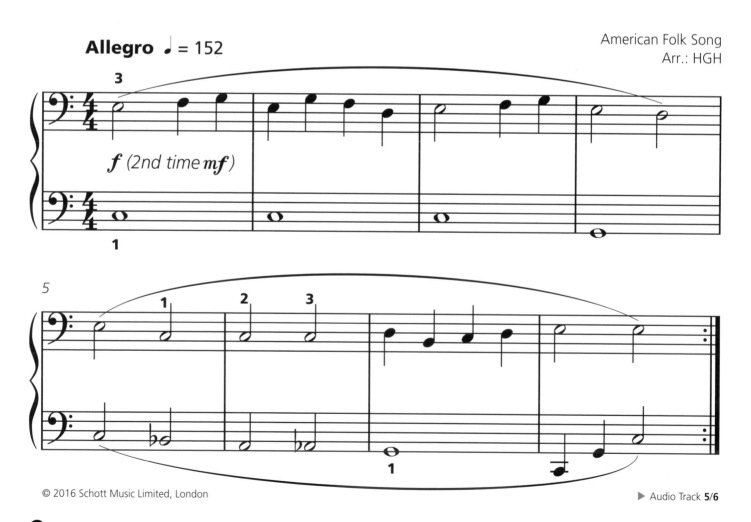

Audio Track **5/6**

8

3. Yankee Doodle

American Folk Song
Arr.: HGH

4. Aura Lee*

Music by George R. Poulton (1828–1867)
Lyrics by William W. Fosdick (1825–1862)
Arr.: HGH

Andante ♩ = 88

mf legato

*) The hit song *Love Me Tender* by Elvis Presley used this tune with different words.

▶ Audio Track **7/8**

4. Aura Lee*

Music by George R. Poulton (1828–1867)
Lyrics by William W. Fosdick (1825–1862)
Arr.: HGH

Andante

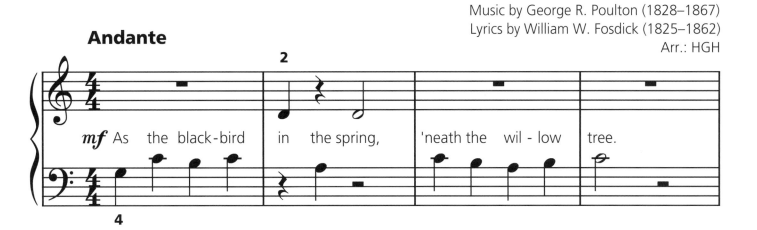

As the black-bird | in the spring, | 'neath the wil-low | tree.

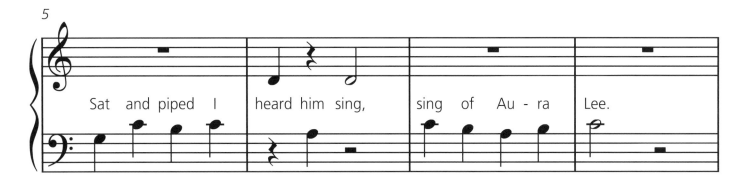

Sat and piped I | heard him sing, | sing of Au-ra | Lee.

Au-ra Lee, | Au-ra Lee, | maid of gol-den | hair,

sun-shine came a | long with thee, and | swal-low in the | air.

*) The hit song *Love Me Tender* by Elvis Presley used this tune with different words.

5. Mélodie

No. 11 from *L'ABC du Piano*

Allegretto ♩ = 144

Félix Le Couppey (1811–1887)

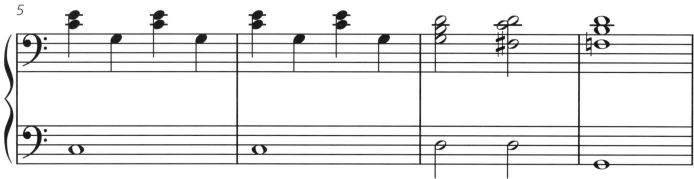

▶ Audio Track **9/10**

12

5. Mélodie

No. 11 from *L'ABC du Piano*

Allegretto

Félix Le Couppey (1811–1887)

13

6. Andante

from *Preparatory School* Op. 101, No. 32

♩ = 88

Ferdinand Beyer (1803–1863)

p dolce e legato

▶ Audio Track **11/12**

6. Andante

from *Preparatory School* Op. 101, No. 32

Ferdinand Beyer (1803–1863)

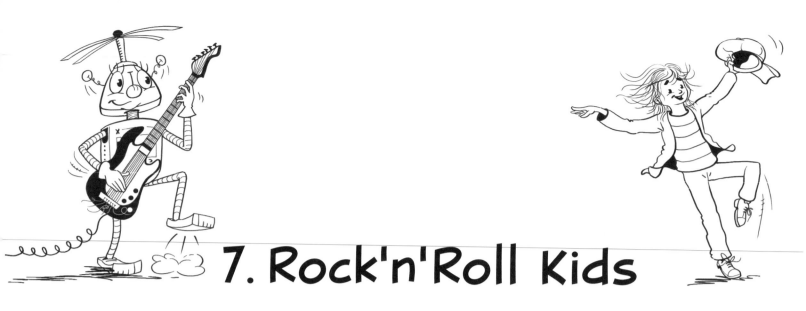

7. Rock'n'Roll Kids

▶ Audio Track **13/14**

18

7. Rock'n'Roll Kids

8. Scherzo

from *10 Little Pieces*, Vol.4

Allegretto ♩ = 126

Henk Badings (1907–1987)

poco *f* leggiero

poco rit.

▶ Audio Track **15/16**

8. Scherzo

from *10 Little Pieces*, Vol.4

Allegretto

Henk Badings (1907–1987)

9. The Elephant

from *The Carnival of the Animals*

Allegretto pomposo ♩ = 126

Camille Saint-Saëns (1835–1921)
Arr.: HGH

▶ Audio Track **17/18**

9. The Elephant

from *The Carnival of the Animals*

Allegretto pomposo

Camille Saint-Saëns (1835–1921)
Arr.: HGH

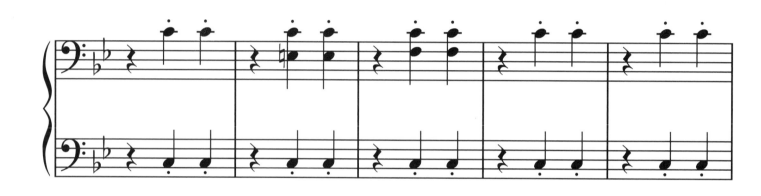

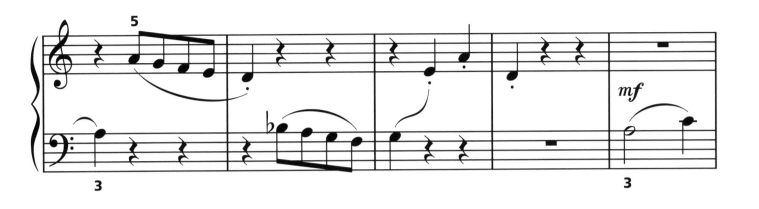

10. The Beginner

Op. 211, No.3

Allegretto ♩ = 144

Cornelius Gurlitt (1820–1901)

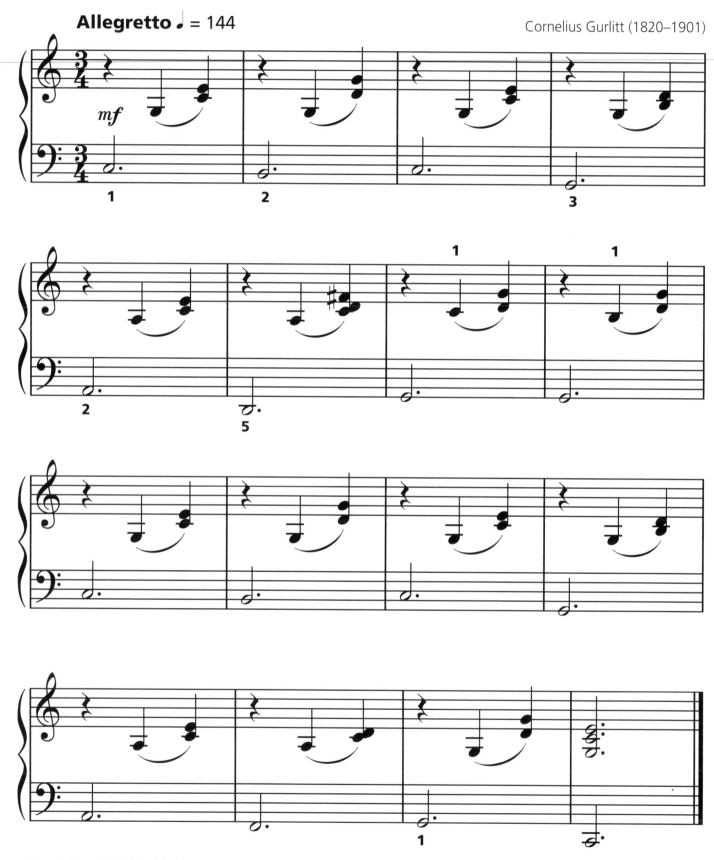

▶ Audio Track **19/20**

10. The Beginner

Op. 211, No.3

Allegretto

Cornelius Gurlitt (1820–1901)

*) When the sign *15* - - - - (Ital. quindicesima) appears over a note or group of notes, play the notes two octaves higher than written.

11. Feelin' Jazzy

▶ Audio Track **21/22**

11. Feelin' Jazzy

HGH

12. Prélude*

from *Te Deum*

Allegretto ♩ = 120

Marc-Antoine Charpentier (1634–1704)
Arr.: HGH

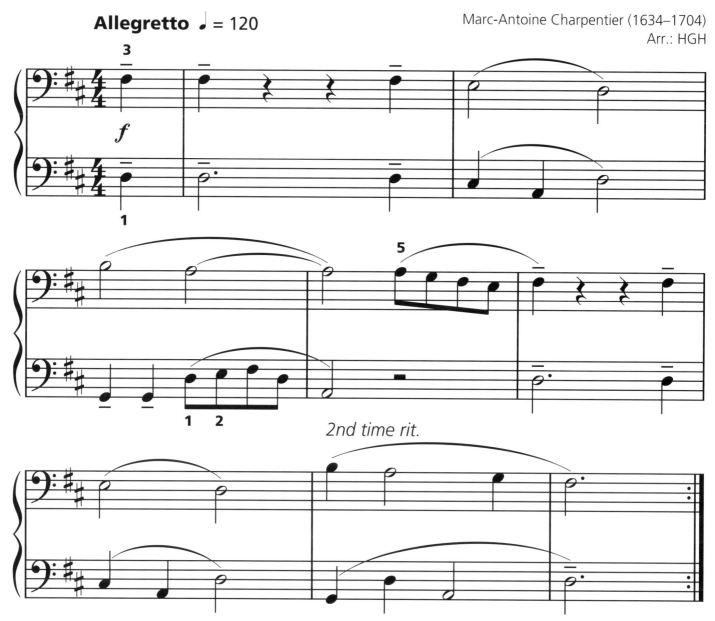

2nd time rit.

*) This has been the Eurovison signature-tune since 1954

▶ Audio Track **23/24**

12. Prélude*

from *Te Deum*

Allegretto

Marc-Antoine Charpentier (1634–1704)

Arr.: HGH

2nd time rit.

*) This has been the Eurovison signature-tune since 1954